THE COMPLETE CHANSONS
Livre troisième des chansons . . . (1590)

RECENT RESEARCHES IN THE MUSIC OF THE RENAISSANCE

James Haar and Howard Mayer Brown, general editors

A-R Editions, Inc., publishes six quarterly series—

Recent Researches in the Music of the Middle Ages and Early Renaissance,
Margaret Bent, general editor;

Recent Researches in the Music of the Renaissance,
James Haar and Howard Mayer Brown, general editors;

Recent Researches in the Music of the Baroque Era,
Robert L. Marshall, general editor;

Recent Researches in the Music of the Classical Era,
Eugene K. Wolf, general editor;

Recent Researches in the Music of the Nineteenth and Early Twentieth Centuries,
Rufus Hallmark, general editor;

Recent Researches in American Music,
H. Wiley Hitchcock, general editor—

which make public music that is being brought to light
in the course of current musicological research.

Each volume in the *Recent Researches* is devoted
to works by a single composer or to a single genre of composition,
chosen because of its potential interest to scholars and performers,
and prepared for publication according to the standards that govern
the making of all reliable historical editions.

Subscribers to this series, as well as patrons of subscribing institutions,
are invited to apply for information about the "Copyright-Sharing Policy"
of A-R Editions, Inc., under which the contents of this volume
may be reproduced free of charge for study or performance.

Correspondence should be addressed:

A-R EDITIONS, INC.
315 West Gorham Street
Madison, Wisconsin 53703

RECENT RESEARCHES IN THE MUSIC OF THE RENAISSANCE • VOLUME LXII

André Pevernage

THE COMPLETE CHANSONS

Livre troisième
des chansons . . . (1590)

Edited by Gerald R. Hoekstra

A-R EDITIONS, INC. • MADISON

ANDRE PEVERNAGE
THE COMPLETE CHANSONS

Edited by Gerald R. Hoekstra

Recent Researches in the Music of the Renaissance

Library of Congress Cataloging in Publication Data:

Pevernage, André, 1542 or 3–1591.
   [Chansons, livre 3e]
   Livre troisième des chansons—(1590)

   (The complete chansons / André Pevernage ; [v. 3])

   (Recent researches in the music of the Renaissance,
ISSN 0486-123X ; v. 62)
   Chansons and motets ; for superius, quinta, contra-
tenor, tenor, and bassus.
   French or Latin words.
   Edited from the 1st ed.
   Words also printed as text with English transla-
tions: p.
   Includes bibliographical references.
   1. Chansons, Polyphonic   2. Motets.   I. Hoekstra,
Gerald R.   II. Series: Pevernage, André, 1542 or 3-1591.
Chansons ; v. 3.   III. Series: Recent researches in the
music of the Renaissance ; v. 62.
M2.R2384   vol. 62   [M1582]   83-9962
ISBN 0-89579-183-8 (set)
ISBN 0-89579-189-7 (v. 3)

Contents

Livre troisième des chansons . . . (1590)

Introduction

Livre troisième des chansons . . . (1590)

Four books of André Pevernage's chansons were published between 1589 and 1591, and four other chansons by Pevernage were included in anthologies published in 1590 and 1597. All of Pevernage's chansons are edited in the present RECENT RESEARCHES IN THE MUSIC OF THE RENAISSANCE series (in RRRen volumes LX–LXIV). This volume includes all of the music of Pevernage's *Livre troisième des chansons*, and this Introduction deals specifically with that source. For information of a more general nature concerning the composer and his music, see the Preface in RRRen volume LX.[1] The *Livre troisième* bears the date 15 June 1590 in its dedication, indicating that it followed Book II by just three and a half months. While Book I is distinguished by its sacred and devotional texts and Book IV by its textures of six, seven, and eight voices, Book III differs little in character from Book II. Both contain primarily secular chansons for five voices. In addition, Book III contains four Latin motets at the end of the volume.

The five partbooks of the *Livre troisième des chansons* bear the designations Superius, Contratenor, Tenor, Bassus, and Quinta. The range of the Quinta is variable, moving from piece to piece between the ranges of Superius and Tenor. Complete copies of the entire set of partbooks are held by the Bayerische Staatsbibliothek, Munich, and the Österreichische Nationalbibliothek, Vienna. Copies of the Superius, Contratenor, and Bassus partbooks can also be found in the Gemeentemuseum in The Hague.

Pevernage dedicated this third book to one of his benefactors, Antoine de Blondel, Baron of Quincy. A translation of the dedication (reproduced in facsimile as Plate II) reads:

> To my Lord Antoine de Blondel, Baron of Cuincy, etc.
>
> My Lord, remembering often, that among a thousand other virtues that are sought after by everyone, the delight that (I know) you have for Music, together with the singular benevolence that I myself have found in your L[ordship] since our youth, have led me to confess, voluntarily and openly, that I have for a long time had a very strong

> desire to find the means by which I can make apparent to you, by a living and clear testimony of gratitude, the sincere affection that I hold for you. Thus, having ruminated upon, pondered, and digested thoroughly this deliberation, I have finally resolved to present to you this my little book of Chansons: which, albeit not worthy of the greatness of your virtues and even less of declaring to you the desire that I have to be of some humble and grateful service, is fitting for your virtuous merits; I beseech you and beseech you again, M[y] L[ord], to receive it with such good will as I offer it. And having seen that you delight no less in grave and modest Music than in light and entertaining music, I have thought it well to add at the end some Motets. Otherwise, having no other desire than to do something by which I might be incorporated and imprisoned in the bosom of your more courteous and good graces, to which very humbly and sincerely I commend myself: Praying the Creator, M[y] L[ord], to have and to hold you in his holiness and safekeeping and protection. Antwerp, June 15, 1590.
>
> Your humble and affectionate servant
> André Pevernage

Of the twenty-five separate pieces in Book III, ten are constituent parts of composite works in more than one section (*pièces liées*). There are two *pièces liées* in two *partes* (or *parties*, as Pevernage calls them), nos. 5–6 and 7–8; and one chanson, the epithalamion celebrating the marriage of the Governor of Courtrai, in six *parties*, nos. 16–21. The epithalamion is the longest composition in Pevernage's chanson books.

Like the chansons of the other Pevernage books, the chansons of *Livre troisième* appear to be grouped by mode and voice ranges; this grouping does not include the motets, however. Chansons with the same final and similar ranges are placed together in Book III. The mode designations in the list on p. viii are not present in the source, of course, and the distinction between plagal and authentic modes here is made solely on the basis of the voice ranges and tessituras, which lie approximately a fourth lower in the plagal modes than in their authentic counterparts. The present editor selected the Tenor as the mode-determining voice, as did Glareanus and others in the sixteenth century.

Nos. 1–4	Dorian on G
Nos. 5–8	Mixolydian on G
Nos. 9–11	Hypomixolydian on G
Nos. 12–14	Phrygian on E
Nos. 15–21	Hypoaeolian on A

Except for Dorian on G, none of the modes of Book III duplicates those used in Book II, which has eight different modal groups (see RRRen vol. LXI, Introduction). Thus, while the contents of Books II and III are otherwise similar, evidence of the overall planning of the four chanson publications appears in this distinction of modes.

While most of the texts set in Book III deal explicitly or implicitly with the vicissitudes of love, a dominant theme in Book II as well, several focus on other subjects. *D'estre si longtemps en tutelle* (no. 1) seems at least superficially to be a *chanson spirituelle*—the meaning of "tutelle" in its first line is ambiguous—and thus its inclusion in Book III rather than in Book I is surprising. This quatrain

produce any passage specifically. *Dulce tuum nostro scribas* (no. 23) appears to be a devotional poem, although it lacks rhyme. The last of the four Latin texts, *Benedictio, et claritas* (no. 25), is a table grace similar in character to two others that appear in Pevernage's *Livre quatrième*.

Only four of the chanson texts can be attributed to poets of the time. Table 1 designates the poet and poetic form or genre for each of these four texts.[2] Pevernage selected only the first quatrain of each of the two *chansons* in this list for musical setting. Of the Ronsard *sonnet*, he set only the first *huitain*, breaking it into two quatrains (set, respectively, in nos. 7 and 8). He set all of Desportes's *sonnet*, however, dividing it into the customary *huitain* plus *sizain* (in nos. 5 and 6).

The *Livre troisième* contains three of Pevernage's more madrigalistic chansons: *Comme le Chasseur* (no. 10); *Les oyseaux cherchent* (no. 13); and *Sur tous regretz* (no. 14). The more colorful and dramatic set-

Table 1			
CHANSON	TITLE	POET	FORM OR GENRE
No. 4	Je suis aimé de la plus belle	Marot	*chanson*
Nos. 5–6	Recerche qui voudra	Desportes	*sonnet*
Nos. 7–8	Ces deux yeux bruns	Ronsard	*sonnet*
No. 11	Pour faire qu'un' affection	Desportes	*chanson*

may, of course, have been extracted from a larger poem that bemoans the torments of the lover, a common theme also suggested by *Si vous m'aimez* (no. 3), *Comme le Chasseur* (no. 10), *Les oyseaux cherchent* (no. 13), *Sur tous regretz* (no. 14), and *Si cestuy qui bien ayme* (no. 15). Other texts of Book III that do not deal directly with love are *Chacun corps est mortel* (no. 2), whose exalted humanistic tone seems a surprising contrast with the humility and orthodox character of Pevernage's *chansons spirituelles*, and the typical (for Pevernage) moralistic and didactic poems of *Recerche qui voudra* (nos. 5–6) and *Pour faire qu'un' affection* (no. 11). The only occasional chanson in Book III is the *Epithalamion pour Monsieur de Werp* (nos. 16–21). A piece of functional doggerel, the poem lauds the virtues of the newlyweds and, in a way that seems amusing today, wishes them a fruitful relationship (see Texts and Translations).

The four Latin texts at the end of the *Livre troisième* are all sacred. The first, *Quare tristis es, anima mea* (no. 22) is the refrain of both Psalms 42 and 43. The sources of the other motet texts are not known to this editor. While the text of *Vide Domine afflictionem nostram* (no. 24) resembles many passages of Scripture in its expression, it does not re-

tings, as might be expected, are elicited by the exaggerated and picturesque expressions of the texts. The chasing and fleeing of no. 10 call forth short points of imitation. The references to death, tomb, and piteous weeping in nos. 10, 13, and 14 are made in dark harmonic sonorities and longer notes, and the heaving sighs of no. 14 receive the standard sixteenth-century treatment of repetitions punctuated by rests. Other examples of dramatic text settings pervade these three chansons also. While the remaining texts in Book III provide fewer opportunities than these three, occasional madrigalisms, as well as such rhetorical devices as the declamatory figures that open no. 21, can be found throughout the collection.

Editorial Commentary

This edition of the *Livre troisième des chansons . . .* (1590) is based on the complete set of partbooks in the Bayerische Staatsbibliothek of Munich (shelf number Mus pr 32/2), which was made available to the editor on microfilm. The sixteenth-century original is clearly printed and easily read. Editorial additions and alterations are enclosed in brackets in this volume. However, although titles have been added by the editor, they are not in brackets. The only title that appears in the source is that of no. 16, the *Epithalamion pour Monsieur de Werp;* all others are added by the editor and simply reproduce all or part of the first line of text. The barlines drawn through the staves are also editorial. Horizontal brackets (⌐⌐) mark notes that appear as ligatures in the source.

No problems with text underlay were encountered, because Pevernage's style is predominantly syllabic, and because Plantin took great care for the accuracy of text placement in his publications. In the source, all repetitions of text are either written out or indicated with the sign *ij*. No additional editorial repetitions were necessary.

For the most part, spelling and punctuation of the texts remain unaltered. However, all abbreviations, including ampersands, have been written out, and archaic spellings with "u," "v," and "i" have been changed to their modern forms whenever the original version might confuse the reader, as, for instance, in *ie viue* (*je vive*). The use of contractions and apostrophes to indicate elisions follows the source. Accents have been added to vowels where they were omitted from the source (either by mistake or because the practice was not standard) and where their absence might affect pronunciation or confuse the reader. Spellings have otherwise not been modernized, even though pronunciation should not differ substantially from modern forms of the same words. The most frequently encountered archaism is the obsolete "s," which would not have been pronounced.[3] In this edition syllable divisions in the French texts indicate whether the "s" is to be pronounced or not: where the "s" falls before the division, it is silent; where it falls after the division, it must be pronounced. For example, in *mais-tre* and *vos-tre* the "s" is silent; in *tri-stesse* and *e-sprits* the "s" is pronounced. Another common archaism is seen in spellings with "oi," where modern French has "ai," as in *regnoit* (*regnait*), *resistoit* (*resistait*), or *apparoistre* (*apparaître*). Again, the modern "ai" sound should be used.

Punctuation follows the source for the most part, but some editorial changes were made for the sake of clarity. In many cases, the punctuation following a phrase of text in the source is not clear because the final appearance of the phrase is indicated with the *ij* sign, and thus includes no punctuation. Full stops, usually indicated in the edition with a colon, were added where the comma used in the source seemed insufficient, or where a colon was lacking in the source because the phrase of text makes its last appearance by means of a repeat sign.

The editorial incipit of the music gives the name, clef, key signature, mensuration sign, and first note of each part as found in Plantin's print. For the G- and moveable C- and F-clefs of the source, this edition uses the treble, tenor G-clef, and bass clef. Although its name has been retained, the placement of the Quinta voice varies from piece to piece, depending on its range. Where its range corresponds with that of the Superius, the Quinta is placed on the fourth staff up. Where the range of the Quinta is like that of the Tenor, it appears on the middle staff. Ranges of all voices are indicated immediately before the modern clef. (Performers should note that the range does not always give a reliable impression of the tessitura; for instance, the bottom note of the specified range may appear only once or twice in certain works, and the most common low note in the piece may otherwise be a fourth above that indicated in the range-finder.) Note values in this edition have been reduced by half, except for the final note of each piece, which is a longa in the source and has been transcribed here as a whole-note with a fermata.

Pevernage used two mensuration signs, ℭ and ₵, but with no apparent distinction in musical styles or rhythmic values. It is likely that Pevernage, like many of his contemporaries, did not intend different meanings for the two signs, but they have nevertheless been retained.

Accidentals that appear within the staff are original; those that appear above the staff are editorial and include both cautionary accidentals and *musica ficta*. Editorial accidentals have been supplied sparingly, and consideration has been given to general sixteenth-century practices as well as to Pevernage's own idiosyncrasies. Where sharp signs in the source cancel flats, they have been changed to naturals in the edition. In the source, an accidental is valid only for successive notes of the same pitch, unless the second statement of that pitch begins a new phrase, in which case the validity of the accidental is not always clear. In the source, an accidental is canceled either by a rest or by an intervening note of a different pitch, and this system is also followed here, since it seems clearest in music with such frequent and temporary pitch alterations. Thus, accidentals that are redundant in modern practice are, nevertheless, preserved here. Both original and editorial accidentals should be considered valid for consecutive notes within measures. In a given voice, where previously inflected pitches recur after intervening notes and the accidental must be invalidated, an editorial reminder is provided above the staff.

The shape of the melodic lines in many places may tempt the reader to raise or lower pitches in accordance with the rules of *musica ficta*. However, performers must be careful to take note of the other voices: such alterations will often result in cross-relations within a chord or in augmented harmonies. The extreme care, frequency, and consistency with which Pevernage supplied accidentals make it doubtful that he intended the performer to add many of his own. A notable departure from normal sixteenth-century practice in this respect is his avoidance of diminished harmonies in the first inversion for penultimate chords at cadences (i.e., dim. VII^6–I). Although he invariably supplied a sharp to the third where the penultimate chord lies a fourth below the cadence chord, and where anyone familiar with the style would add one anyway, he consistently left unaltered those penultimate chords that have their roots a major second below the cadence chord. Pevernage's consistency in this matter suggests that he intended the VII^6 to remain unaltered.

Critical Notes

The following list cites errors in the source, accidentals made superfluous by the editorial procedure, and other discrepancies, all of which are minor, between the present edition and the source. Pitches are designated according to the usual sys-

tem, wherein middle C is c', the C above middle C is c'', and so forth.

No. 1—M. 10, Superius, note 2 has a sharp in the source.

No. 8—M. 34, all parts, underlaid text reads "eus" rather than "eux" in the source.

No. 10—M. 33, Superius, note 2 has a sharp in the source. M. 35, all parts, the diminished harmony at the end of the measure is found in the source.

No. 16—M. 23, Tenor, note 1 has a sharp sign that functions as a cautionary natural.

No. 19—M. 22, Superius and Contratenor, beat 1, the C-C♯ cross-relation is found in the source.

No. 21—Mm. 11–15, the spellings "Epous'" and "Espous'" both appear in the source; all appearances of the word have been standardized here to the former spelling.

No. 22—M. 23, Contratenor, note 3 has a superfluous sharp in the source; Bassus, in the original the last syllable falls on the penultimate note.

No. 25—M. 31, Superius, note 1, and hence the second of the ligature, is colored in the source (♮ ♩).

In all chansons where the initial line of text is not set to music in one or more parts, the text is printed under the empty staff at the beginning of those parts in the original partbooks.

Notes

1. Books I, II, and III (RRRen vols. LX–LXII) all contain chansons *a 5*; Book IV (RRRen vols. LXIII–LXIV) consists of chansons *a 6, 7,* and *8.* The four chansons from other collections—three chansons *a 4* and a chanson *a 2* in three *parties*—are included at the end of RRRen vol. LXIV. For further information concerning the composer, his chanson publications, and his musical style, the reader is referred to the more substantial Preface in RRRen vol. LX and to Gerald R. Hoekstra, "The Chansons of André Pevernage (1542/43–1591)" (Ph.D. diss., The Ohio State University, 1975).
2. The two poems by Desportes come, respectively, from his *Diverses amours* (1573) and *Les amours d'Hippolyte* (1573); see the modern editions by Victor E. Graham, *Diverses amours et autres oeuvres mellées* (Geneva: Librairie Droz, 1963) and *Les amours d'Hippolyte* (Geneva: Librairie Droz, 1960). The Ronsard *sonnet* comes from his *Amours,* the source of numerous sixteenth-century song texts. For a modern edi-

tion of the *Amours,* see *Les oeuvres de Pierre de Ronsard: texte de 1587,* ed. Isadore Silver (Chicago: The University of Chicago Press, 1966). Ronsard frequently revised his poetry, and, like many of his poems, this one exists in several different versions. The version that Pevernage set differs considerably from the one that appears in Silver's edition, which is based on the *Oeuvres* of 1587. Marot's *Je suis aimé de la plus belle* is numbered in the standard editions of his works as Chanson X; see C. A. Meyer's edition, *Clement Marot's Oeuvres lyriques* (London: University of London, The Athlone Press, 1964).
3. E.-J. Bourciez, *Phonétique française* (Paris: Editions Klinksieck, n.d.) gives a historical overview of French pronunciation. See also Jeannine Alton and Brian Jeffery, *Bele Buche e Bele Parleure: A Guide to the Pronunciation of Medieval and Renaissance French for Singers and Others* (London: Tecla Editions, 1976).

Texts and Translations

The following translations from the French were made by the editor with the helpful advice and guidance of Dr. William Huseman. They are literal rather than poetic translations. The translation of no. 22, *Quare tristis es, anima mea*, is taken from Psalm 42, verse 11 of the King James Version, and the translations of the other three motet texts were provided by Dr. Derke Bergsma.

Livre troisième des chansons . . . **(1590)**

No.1

D'estre si longtemps en tutelle
Donn' à mon coeur grand tourment:
O Dieu, mets fin à ma querelle,
Pour alleger mon pensement.

(Being so long under guardianship
Torments my heart greatly.
O God, put an end to my struggle,
So that my cares might be lightened.)

No. 2

Chacun corps est mortel,
    l'esprit de vertu pare,
Car l'homme par ainsi
    aux grands Dieux s'equipare.

(Every body is mortal;
    The spirit adorns it with virtue,
For thus man becomes the equal
    Of the great gods.)

No. 3

Si vous m'aimez, faictes le voir,
Payant mon fidelle devoir
De la plus seure recompense:
Ou bien si vous ne m'aimez pas,
Faictes moy sentir le trespas,
Finissant ma longue souffrance.

(If you love me, show me
By repaying my faithful duty
With the surest reward.
Or if you do not love me,
Make me experience death,
Ending my long suffering.)

No. 4 — Clément Marot

Je suis aimé de la plus belle,
Qui soit dessous les cieux,
Encontre tous faux envieux
Je la soustiendray estre telle.

(I am loved by the most beautiful one
Under the skies.
Against all false envious ones
I will maintain that she is such.)

No. 5   [*1. partie*] — Philippe Desportes

Recerche qui voudra les apparans honneurs,
Les pompes, les tresors, les faveurs variables,
Les lieux haut eslevez, les palais remerquables,
Retraites de pensers, d'ennuis et de douleurs:
J'aime mieux voir un pré bien tapissé de fleurs,
Arrousé de ruisseaux à l'argent vif semblables,
Et tout encourtiné de buissons delectables
Pour l'ombr' et pour la soif, durant les grans
    chaleurs.

(Let all who would, seek outward honors,
Pomp, treasures, changeable favor,
Exalted position, spectacular palaces,
Bastions of worries, troubles, and sorrows:
I would rather see a meadow carpeted with flowers,
Watered by a stream resembling quicksilver,
Surrounded with delightful thickets of trees,
For shade and for thirst during the summer.)

No. 6   *2. partie*

Là, franc d'ambition, je voy couler ma vie,
Sans envier aucun, sans qu'on me port' envie,
Roy de tous mes desirs, content de mon parti.
Je ne m'appaste point d'une vain' esperance,
Fortune ne peut rien contre mon asseurance,
Et mon repos d'esprit n'est jamais diverti.

(There, free of ambition, I see my life flowing,
Without envying anyone or having anyone else
    envy me,

King of all my desires, content with my lot;
I am not allured at all by vain hope,
Fortune can do nothing to threaten my security,
And my spiritual rest is never disturbed.)

No. 7   [*1. partie*]   Pierre de Ronsard

Ces deux yeux bruns, deux flambeaux de ma vie,
Dessus les miens respandant leur clarté,
Ont arresté ma jeune liberté,
Pour la damner en prison asservie.

(These two brown eyes, two torches of my life,
Spreading their light above mine,
Have put an end to my youthful freedom,
Condemning it, subjugated, to prison.)

No. 8   *2. partie*

De ces deux yeux ma raison fut ravie,
Si qu' esblouy de leur grande beauté,
Opiniastr' à garder loyauté,
Autres yeux voir depuis je n'eux envie.

(By these two eyes my reason was ravished,
So that, dazzled by their great beauty,
Steadfastly remaining faithful,
I have since then had no desire to see other eyes.)

No. 9

Tousjours l'amant vit en l'aimée,
Pour cela mon am' affamée
Ne se veut saouler que d'amour;
De l'amour ell' est si friande,
Que sans plus de telle viande
Se veut repaistre nuict et jour.

(Always the lover lives in the loved one;
Thus my famished soul
Would gorge itself only on love;
Of love it is so desirous,
That on no other food
Would it feast itself night and day.)

No. 10

Comme le Chasseur va suyvant
La beste qui volle devant,
Laissant celle qui se vient rendre:
Ainsi la mort, qui tout destruit,
Chass' apres celuy qui la fuit,
Et se dedaigne de me prendre.

(As the hunter chases
The beast that flees ahead,
Leaving the one that offers itself,

So death, which destroys all,
Chases after him who flees it
And disdains to take me.)

No. 11   Philippe Desportes

Pour faire qu'un' affection
Ne sujett' à l'inconstance,
Il faut beaucoup de cognoissance,
Et beaucoup de discretion.

(In order for an affection
Not to be subject to inconstancy,
Much understanding is needed
And much discretion.)

No. 12

Faut il qui soit que vous ayez mon coeur,
Content je suis; ne luy faites rigueur,
Mais seulement le vueillez secourir,
Pour eviter le danger de mourir.

(If it is inevitable that you have my heart,
I am content; do not treat it harshly,
But be so good as to protect it,
To avoid the danger of death.)

No. 13

Les oyseaux cherchent la verdure,
Moy je cherch' une sepulture,
Pour voir mon malheur limité:
Vers le ciel ils ont leur volée,
Et mon ame trop desolée
N'ayme rien que l'obscurité.

(The birds seek out green spaces,
Me, I look for a tomb,
In order to see my bad fortune contained.
Toward the sky they take flight,
And my most desolate soul
Desires nothing but obscurity.)

No. 14

Sur tous regretz, le mien plus piteux pleure,
Jettant souspirs, tresperchant mon las coeur,
Car j'ay perdu l'amiable liqueur,
Que tant je plains et plaindray en ampl' heure.

(Of all regrets, mine weep most piteously,
Heaving sighs, piercing deeply my weary heart.
For I have lost the amiable liquor,
For which I weep so much and will weep for long
    hours.)

No. 15

Si cestuy qui bien ayme,
Encore que jouissance
Soit le but de sa peine,
Non pas sans triste souffrance,
Souffrant mal qui attire,
Estre ne peut sans attente,
Ay-je doncq tort de dire
Que bien fort l'attente tente?

(If he who loves well—
Even though pleasure
Be the goal of his efforts,
Though not without sad suffering,
Enduring sweet pain—
Cannot be without expectation,
Am I therefore wrong to say
That expectation tempts strongly?)

No. 16   [*1. partie*]

*Epithalamion pour Monsieur de Werp, Gouverneur
de Courtray*

Sus, filles de Memoire,
Et de Jupin aydant,
Chantons ores la gloire
De Werp, sag' et prudent:
Chantons l'honneur
Aussi de l'Espousée,
Qui de bon coeur
Le prent ceste journée.

(*Epithalamion for Mr. de Werp, Governor of Courtrai*)

(Hark, daughters of Memory
And those aiding Jupiter,
Let us sing now the praises
Of de Werp, wise and prudent.
Let us sing in honor
Also of his bride,
Who willingly
Takes him this day.)

No. 17   *2. partie*

Journée trop heureuse,
Puis qu'en vous nous voyons
Ceste coupl' amoureuse,
De laquell' esperons
Brievement voir
Douce progeniture
Par le devoir
De Venus et nature.

(Day most blessed,
Since in you we see
This loving couple,
Of whom we soon
Hope to see
Sweet progeny
By fulfillment of the duty
Of Venus and nature.)

No. 18   *3. partie*

Au Pere magnanime,
Courtois et gracieux,
Tenu en grand' estime
Pour ses faits valeureux.
Ressembleront
Et des faits et de face
Les fils qu'ilz front,
Par la celeste grace.

(The magnamimous Father,
Courteous and gracious,
Held in great esteem
Because of his valorous deeds;
The sons they produce
By celestial grace
Will resemble him
In deeds and in appearance.)

No. 19   *4. partie*

A la tresdouce Mere,
De Zoete de surnom,
Tresbelle nett' et claire,
Digne de grand' renom;
Semblablement
Ressembleront encore
Entierement
Ses filles que j'honore.

(And the most gentle Mother,
Surnamed de Zoete,
Beautiful, clean, and bright,
Worthy of great renown;
Similarly,
Her daughters, whom I honor,
Will resemble her
Completely.)

No. 20   *5. partie*

La couch' encourtinée,
Où les Graces, l'Amour,
Et la Mere d'Enée,
T'attendent a l'entour,
Il ne faut point
Eviter ce me semble,
Ains sans pourpoint
La frequenter ensemble.

(The curtained couch
Where the Graces, Amor,
And the mother of Aeneas
Await you,
Must not be avoided,
It seems to me,
But rather, without cloak
Frequent it together.)

No. 21   6. partie

C'est faict! ô Hymenée!
Io! Io! Pean!
Nous voirons acouchée,
L'Epous' au bout de l'an,
Va de bon coeur,
Chanson, des l'hyperbore,
Divulguer l'heur
Jusques à sable more.

(It is done! O Hymen!
Io! Io! Pean!
By the end of the year
We shall see the wife in childbed.
Go with good will,
Chanson, all the way from the Northern Seas
Divulge the news
Even to the Moorish sands.)

No. 22

Quare tristis es, anima mea,
    et quare conturbas me?
Spera in Deo, quoniam adhuc confitebor illi,
Salutare vultus mei et Deus meus.

(Why art thou cast down, O my soul,
    and why art thou disquieted within me?

Hope thou in God: for I shall yet praise him
    who is the health of my countenance, and my God.)

No. 23

Dulce tuum nostro scribas in pectore nomen,
Namque tuo constat nomine nostra salus.
Illi triste nihil cadit unquam, mitis JESU,
Qui velit usque tui nominis esse memor.

(Write your sweet name in our hearts,
For our salvation rests in your name.
Nothing mournful ever happens to him, gentle
    JESUS,
Who desires always to be mindful of your name.)

No. 24

Vide Domine afflictionem nostram,
Et in tempore maligno ne derelinquas nos,
Sed veni et noli tardare
Relaxa facinora plebis tuae et revoca dispersos in
    terram suam.

(Behold, Lord, our affliction,
And in the evil time do not forsake us,
But come and do not delay,
Forgive the deeds of your people and restore
    those scattered in your earth.)

No. 25

Benedictio, et claritas, et sapientia, et gratiarum
    actio, honor, et virtus, et fortitudo, Deo nostro,
    in saecula saeculorum. Amen.

(Praise, and renown, and wisdom, and thanks-
    giving, honor, and excellence, and strength to
    our God, world without end. Amen.)

LIVRE TROISIEME
DES CHANSONS
D'ANDRE' PEVERNAGE,
MAISTRE DE LA CHAPELLE
DE L'EGLISE CATHEDRALE
D'ANVERS.

A cincq parties.

SVPERIVS.

A ANVERS,
De l'Imprimerie de Christofle Plantin
M. D. XC.

Plate I. André Pevernage: *Livre troisième des chansons . . .* (1590)
Superius partbook, title page.
(Bayerische Staatsbibliothek, Munich)

A MONSEIGNEVR,
MONSEIGNEVR
ANTOINE DE BLONDEL,
BARON DES CVINCYS, &c.

MONSEIGNEVR, *Rememorant assez souuent, qu'entre mille autres vertus qui vous rendent huy d'vn chascun bien quis, honoré, & bien veu : la delectation que (scay) portez à la Musicque, parensemble la singuliere beneuolence qu'ay mesme trouué des nostre ieunesse en voster S^{tie}, me stimulent de raison volontairement & apertement confesser, qu'ay pieça euë tresardante enuye de trouuer moyen, par lequel ie vous puisse faire apparoir par vif & euident tesmoignage de gratitude, la bonne affection que ie vous porte. Or ceste deliberation grand temps ruminée, pesée, & bien digerée, me suis à la parfin resolu vous presenter ce mien liuret de Chansons: lequel iaçoit que ne soit digne de la grandeur de voz vertus, ne moins bastant à vous declarer le desir qu'ay de vous faire quelque humble & grate seruice, conforme à voz vertueux merites, vous supplie & ressupplie, MONSEIGNEVR, le receuoir de telle part, que de bonne volonté le vous offre. Et ayant experimenté que ne vous delectez pas moins de Musicque graue & modeste, que de legere & recreatiue, i'ay bien voulu adiouster à la fin quelques Motets: Aultre n'affectant que de pouuoir faire chose par laquelle ie puisse estre incorporé & incarceré au fin fond de vostre tresbumaine & bonne grace, à laquelle treshumblement & de cœur me recommande: Priant le Createur, MONSEIGNEVR, vous auoir & maintenir soubs sa saincte & sauue garde & protection. D'Anuers, ce 15. de Iuing,* M. D. X C.

Vostre treshumble & tresaffectionné seruiteur

André Peuernage.

Plate III. André Pevernage: *Livre troisième des chansons . . .* (1590)
Superius partbook, first page of *D'estre si longtemps en tutelle*, no. 1.
(Bayerische Staatsbibliothek, Munich)

LIVRE TROISIEME DES CHANSONS . . . (1590)

1. D'estre si longtemps en tutelle

2. Chacun corps est mortel

3. Si vous m'aimez

re- com- pen- se: Ou bien si vous

re- com- pen- se, De la [plus seu- re re- com- pen- se:] Ou bien si vous

re- com- pen- se, De la [plus seu- re re- com- pen- se:] Ou ___ bien si vous, _____

re- com- pen- se, De [la plus seu- re re- com- pen- se:] Ou bien si

De la plus seu- re re- com- pen- se: Ou bien si vous

ne m'ai- mez pas, _____ Ou bien si vous ne m'ai- mez pas,

ne m'ai- mez pas, Ou [bien si vous ne m'ai- - mez pas,] Faic- tes moy sen-

Ou bien si vous ne m'ai- - mez pas, Faic- tes moy sen-

vous ne m'ai- mez pas, Faic- tes moy sen-

ne m'ai- mez pas, Faic- tes moy sen-

Faic- tes moy sen- tir le tres- pas, Faic- tes [moy sen- tir le tres- pas,]

- tir le tres- pas, Faic- tes [moy sen- tir le tres- pas,] Faic- tes moy sen- tir le tres- pas,

- tir le tres- pas, Faic- tes [moy sen- tir le tres- pas,] Faic- tes moy sen- tir le tres- pas,

- tir le tres- pas, Faic- tes [moy sen- tir le tres- pas,] Faic- tes moy sen- tir le tres- pas,

- tir le tres- pas, Faic- tes moy sen- tir le tres- pas,

4. Je suis aimé de la plus belle

tel- le, _____ es- tre tel- le, es- tre tel- le.

-le,] _____ es- tre tel - - le.

-tien- dray] _____ es - tre tel- le, es- tre tel- le.

- tre tel- - - - le.

es- tre tel- - - le.

5. Recerche qui voudra

[Philippe Desportes]
[1. partie]

Superius

Re- cer- che qui vou- dra les ap- pa- rans hon-

Quinta

Re- cer- che qui vou- dra les

Contratenor

Re- cer- che qui vou- dra les ap- pa-

Tenor

Re- cer- che qui vou- dra, [Re- cer- che qui vou- dra]

Bassus

6. Là, franc d'ambition

24

7. Ces deux yeux bruns

26

8. De ces deux yeux

Superius

[Pierre de Ronsard]
2. partie

De ces deux yeux, De [ces deux yeux] ma rai-son fut ra-

Contratenor

De ces deux yeux, De [ces deux yeux,] De ces deux yeux. ma___

Quinta

De ces deux yeux ma_____ rai-son fut ra- vi-

Tenor

De ces deux yeux ma rai- son___ fut ra- vi- e,

Bassus

De ces deux yeux ma rai- son fut ra- vi-

5

- vi- e, ma_____ [rai- son fut ra- vi- e,] Si qu'es-blou-y___

___ rai- son fut ra- vi- e, Si qu'es-blou-y___

- e, ma [rai- son fut ra- vi- e,] fut ra- vi- e, Si qu'es-blou-y___

ma rai- son_____ fut_____ ra- vi- e,

- e, ma [rai- son fut ra- vi- e,] Si qu'es-blou-y___

28

9. Tousjours l'amant vit en l'aimée

10. Comme le Chasseur

11. Pour faire qu'un' affection

_beau-coup____ de di-scre- ti- on, Et beau- coup de di-scre- ti- on.

- on, Et beau- coup de di- scre- ti- on, de di- scre- ti- on.

- on, Et beau- coup de____ di- scre- ti- on, de di-scre- ti- on.

- on, Et beau-coup de di-scre-ti- on,____ Et beau- coup de di- scre- ti- on.

- on,] Et beau- coup de di- scre- ti- on.

12. Faut il qui soit

Superius: Faut il qui soit, [Faut____ il qui soit,] Faut

Contratenor: Faut il qui soit, [Faut il qui____ soit,] Faut____

Quinta: Faut il____ qui soit, [Faut____ il qui soit,] Faut il

Tenor: Faut il qui soit,

Bassus: Faut il qui soit, [Faut____

13. Les oyseaux cherchent

48

14. Sur tous regretz

52

15. Si cestuy qui bien ayme

_ l'at-ten- te ten- te?] Que bien fort l'at-ten- te ten- te? _____

_ l'at-ten- te ten- te?] Que bien fort ___ l'at-ten- te ten- te?

_ l'at-ten- te ten- - te? Que bien fort l'at-ten- te ten- te?

bien fort l'at-ten- te ten- te? _____

_ l'at-ten- te ten- te?] Que bien fort l'at-ten- te ten- te?

16. Epithalamion pour Monsieur de Werp, Gouverneur de Courtray

Superius [1. partie]
Sus, _____ fil- les de Me-moi-

Quinta
Sus, _____ fil- les de Me-moi-

Contratenor
Sus, _____ fil- les de Me-moi-

Tenor
Sus, _____ fil- les de Me- moi-

Bassus
Sus, _____ fil- les de Me- moi-

60

17. Journée trop heureuse

62

18. Au Pere magnanime

19. A la tresdouce Mere

20. La couch' encourtinée

21. C'est faict! ô Hymenée!

22. Quare tristis es, anima mea

80

23. Dulce tuum nostro scribas

24. Vide Domine afflictionem nostram

25. Benedictio, et claritas

DATE DUE

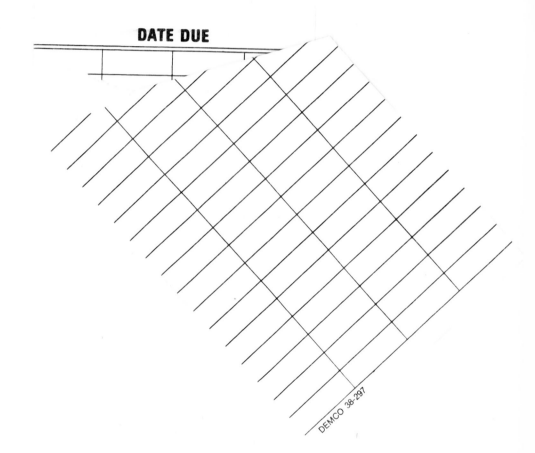